THE HOSTESS BOOK

A handsome house to lodge a friend,
A river at my gardens end
A terrace walk, and half a rood
Of land, set out to plant a wood.

Imitations of Horace
Johnathan Swift 1667-1745

Date of party	GUEST LIST	Replies
_____	_____	_____
_____	_____	_____
_____	_____	_____
_____	_____	_____
_____	_____	_____
_____	_____	_____
_____	_____	_____
_____	_____	_____
_____	_____	_____
_____	_____	_____
_____	_____	_____
_____	_____	_____
_____	_____	_____

PLACEMENT

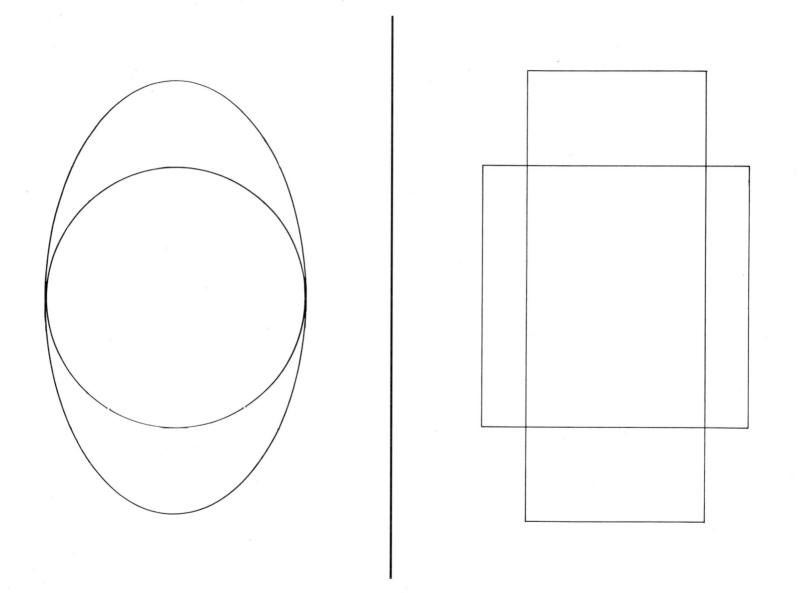

MENU

RECIPES

BUDGET

Still Life with Bread and Cheese
Floris van Schooten (fl.c.1612)

Date of party	GUEST LIST	Replies
_____	_____	_____
_____	_____	_____
_____	_____	_____
_____	_____	_____
_____	_____	_____
_____	_____	_____
_____	_____	_____
_____	_____	_____
_____	_____	_____
_____	_____	_____
_____	_____	_____
_____	_____	_____
_____	_____	_____

PLACEMENT

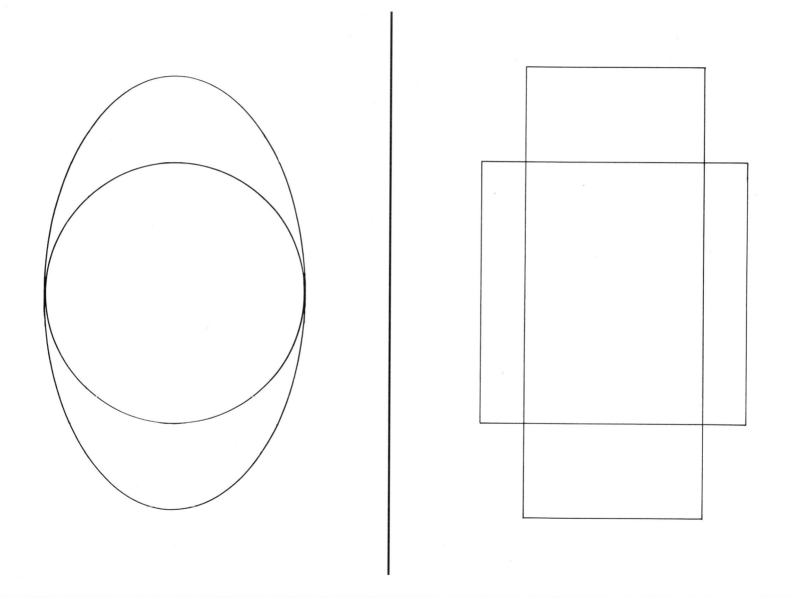

MENU

RECIPES

BUDGET

The Pot of Olives
Jean Baptiste Siméon Chardin (1699-17

Date of party

GUEST LIST

Replies

PLACEMENT

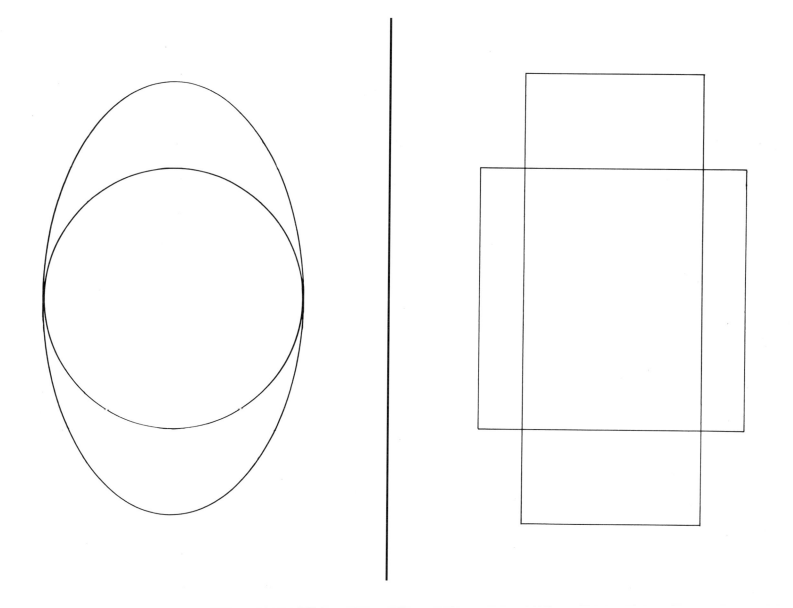

MENU

RECIPES

BUDGET

_____   _____   _____   _____

_____   _____   _____   _____

_____   _____   _____   _____

The Terrace in Front of the Bay at St T
Henri le Sidaner. (1862-1939)
Courtesy of a Private Collector, France.
© D.A.C.S. 1989

Date of party

GUEST LIST

Replies

PLACEMENT

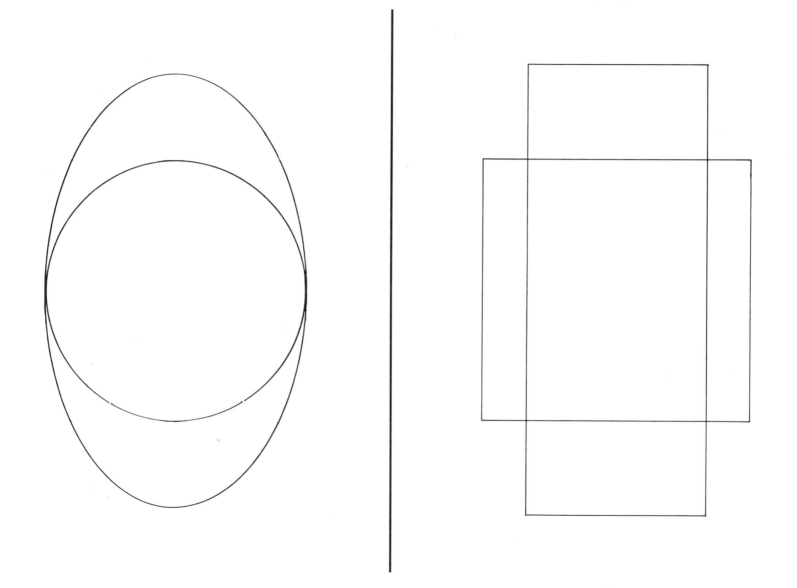

MENU

RECIPES

BUDGET

_____

_____

_____

_____

_____

_____

_____

_____

_____

_____

_____

_____

_____

Peach Still Life
Henri Fantin Latour (1836-1904)

Date of party

GUEST LIST

Replies

_____

_____

_____

_____

_____

_____

_____

_____

_____

_____

_____

_____

_____

_____

_____

PLACEMENT

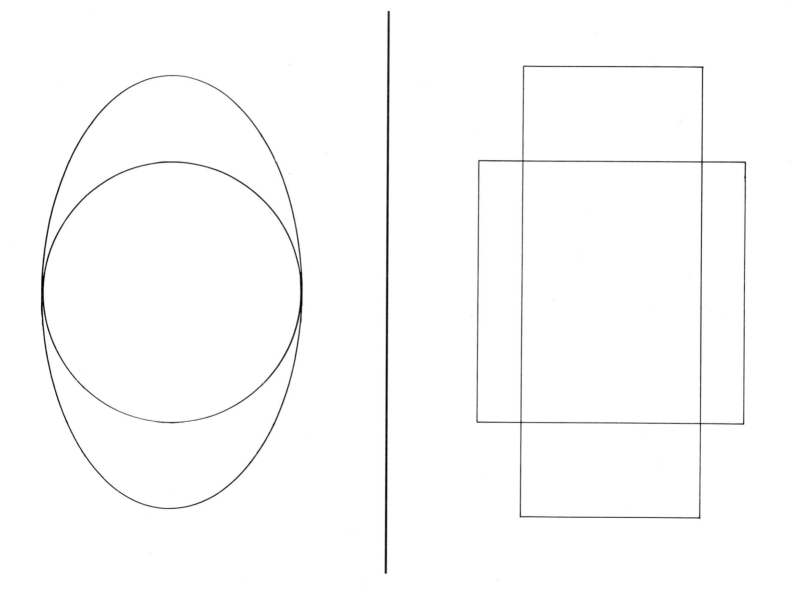

MENU

RECIPES

BUDGET

The Roses
Henri Fantin Latour (1836-1904)

GUEST LIST

Date of party		Replies

PLACEMENT

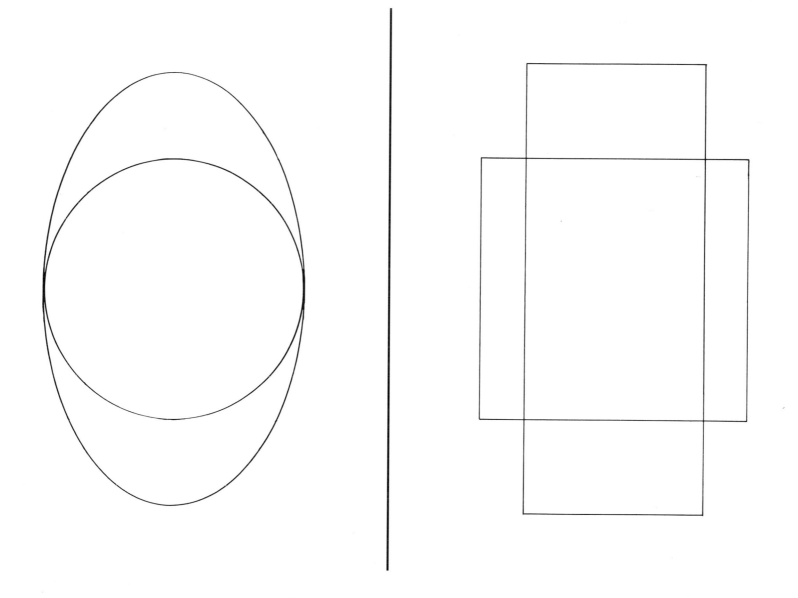

MENU

RECIPES

BUDGET

Interior with a Tea Table
Marcel Rieder (b.1852)

Date of party

GUEST LIST

Replies

PLACEMENT

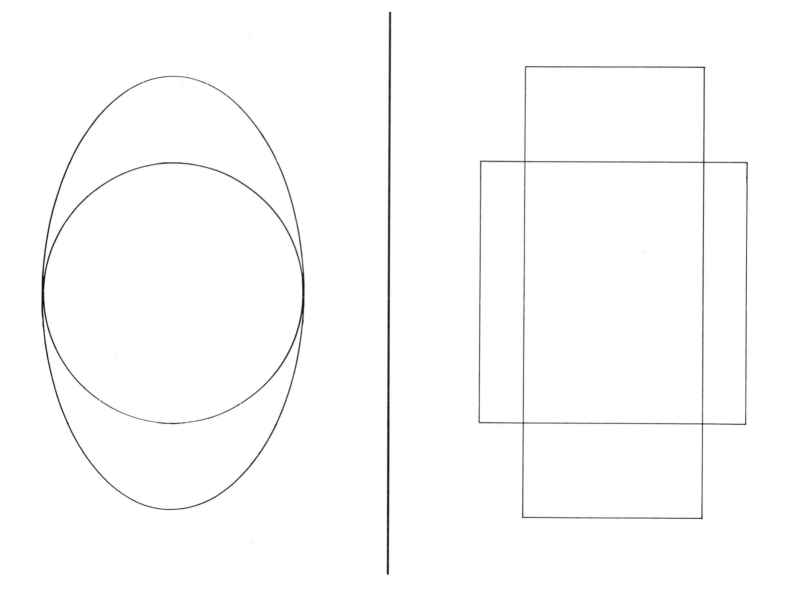

MENU

RECIPES

BUDGET

Still Life
Henri Fantin Latour (1836-1904)

GUEST LIST

Date of party

Replies

PLACEMENT

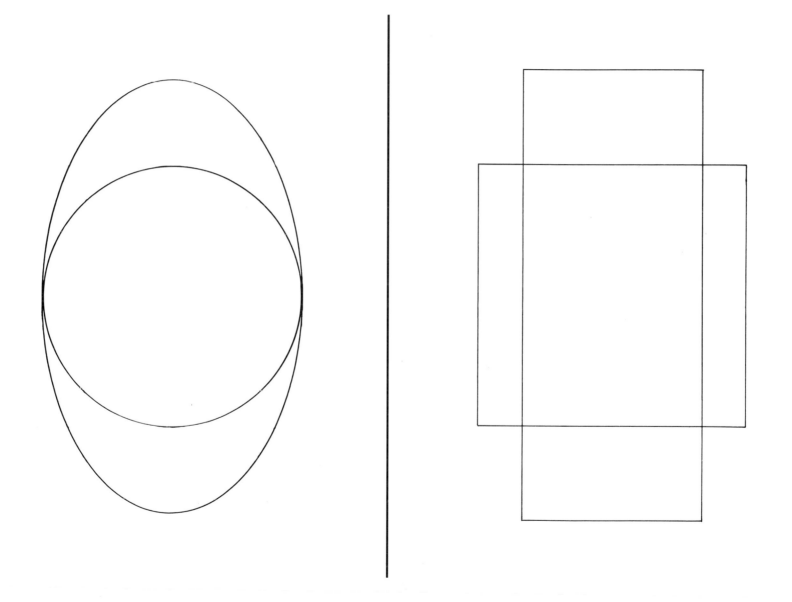

MENU

RECIPES

BUDGET

Tag's Island
Sir Alfred Munnings (1878-1959)

GUEST LIST

Date of party		Replies

PLACEMENT

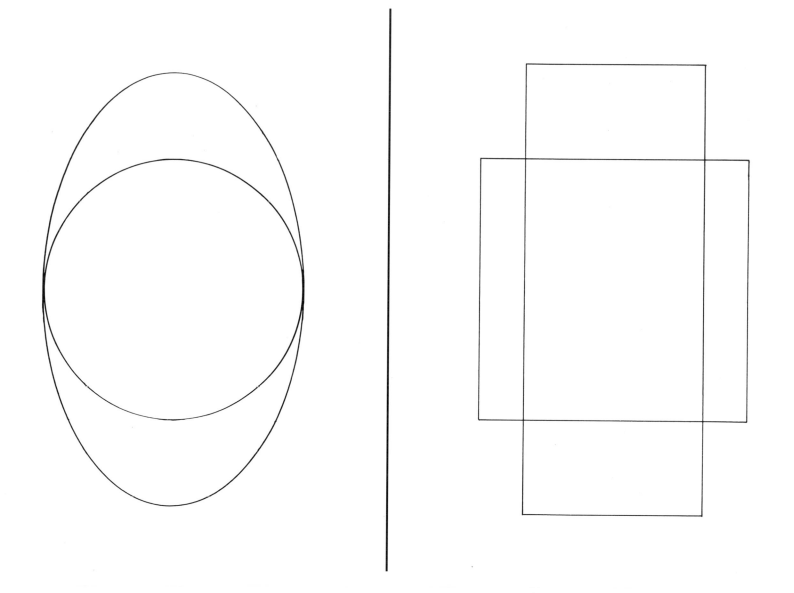

MENU

RECIPES

BUDGET

Still Life with the Drinking Horn
of the Saint Sebastian Archers' Guild,
Lobster and Glasses
Willem Kalf (1619-1693)

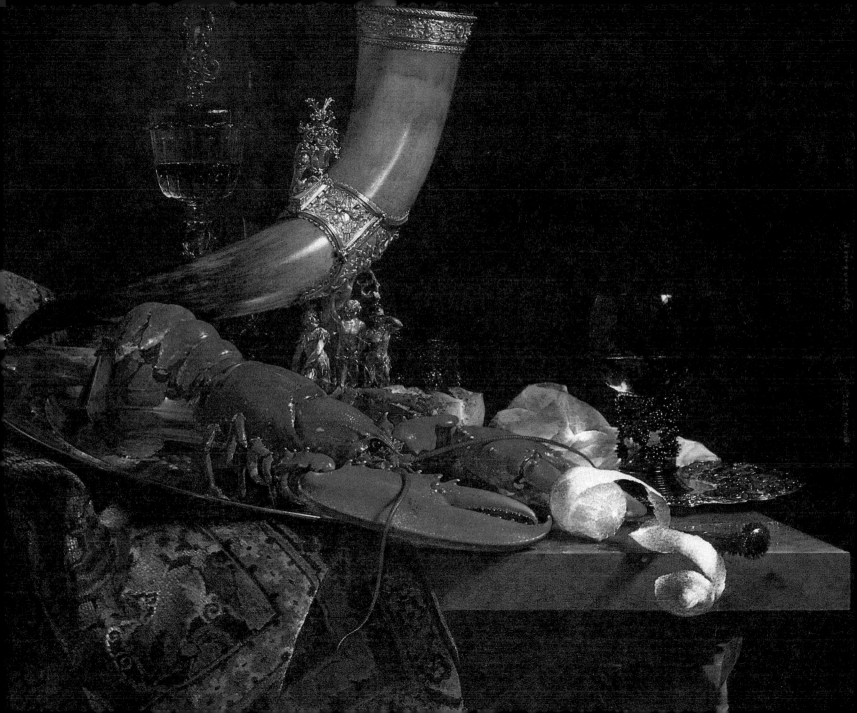

Date of party

GUEST LIST

Replies

PLACEMENT

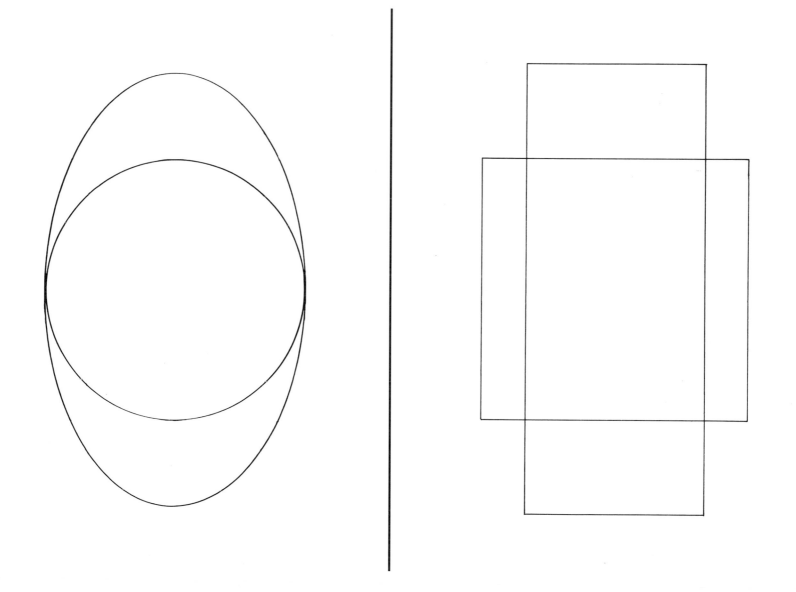

MENU

RECIPES

BUDGET

The Silver Goblet
Jean Baptiste Siméon Chardin (1699-

GUEST LIST

Date of party		Replies

PLACEMENT

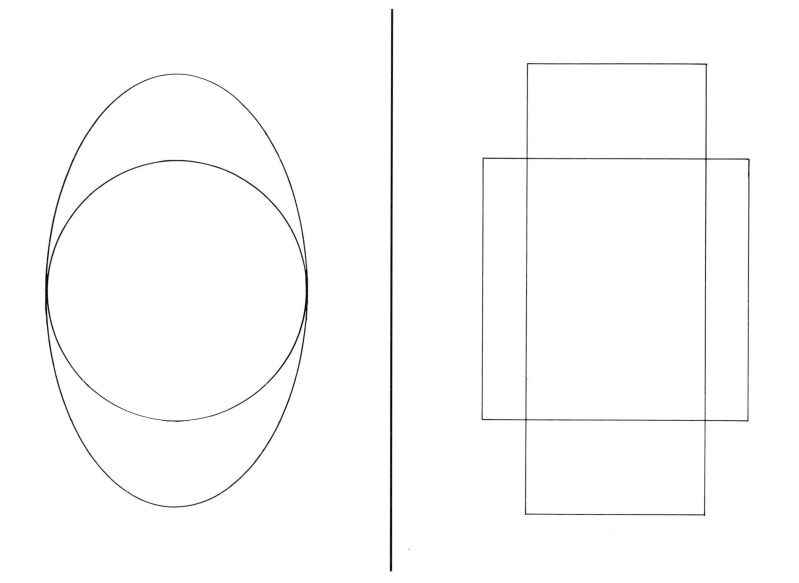

MENU

RECIPES

BUDGET

Still Life with Figs (detail)
Luis Melendez (1716-1780)

Date of party

GUEST LIST

Replies

PLACEMENT

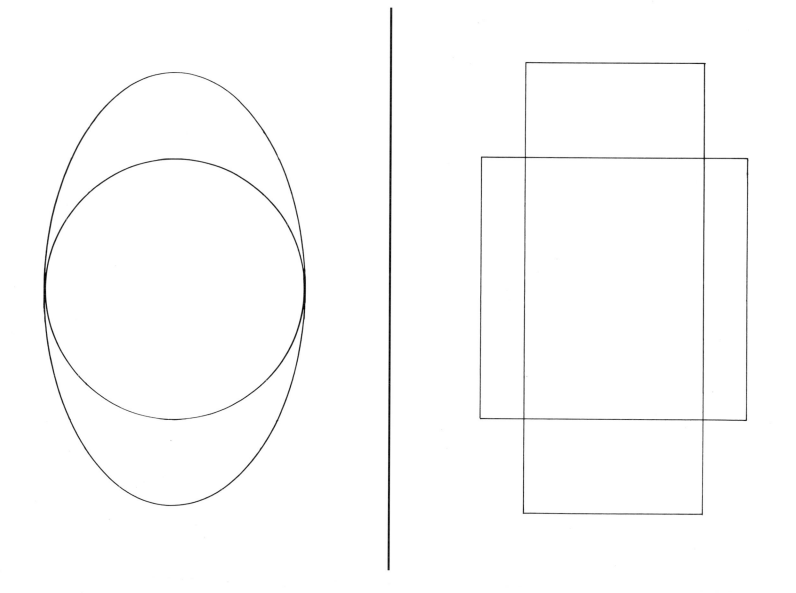

MENU

RECIPES

BUDGET

Still Life with Fruit and Bottles
Charles Couche (19th century)

Date of party

GUEST LIST

Replies

PLACEMENT

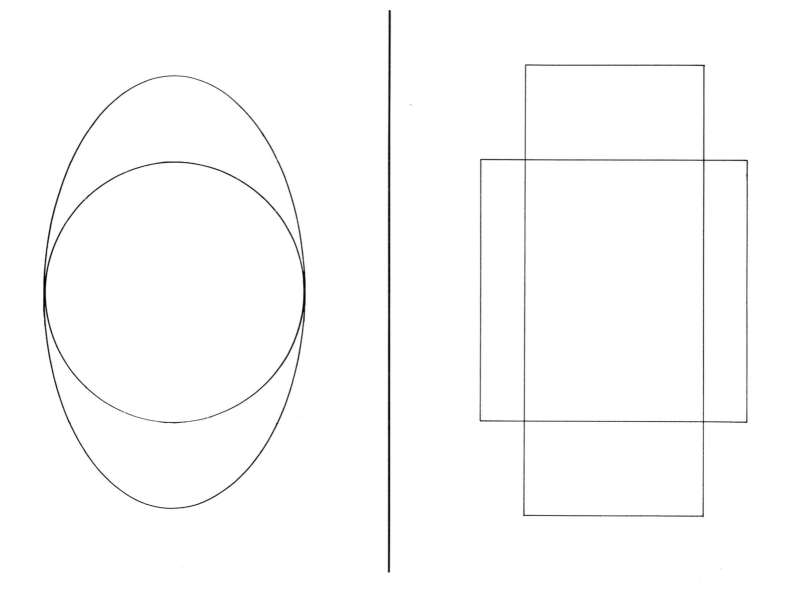

MENU

RECIPES

BUDGET

Still Life with Lemons,
Oranges and a Rose (detail)
Francisco de Zurbaran (1598-1664)

GUEST LIST

Date of party

Replies

PLACEMENT

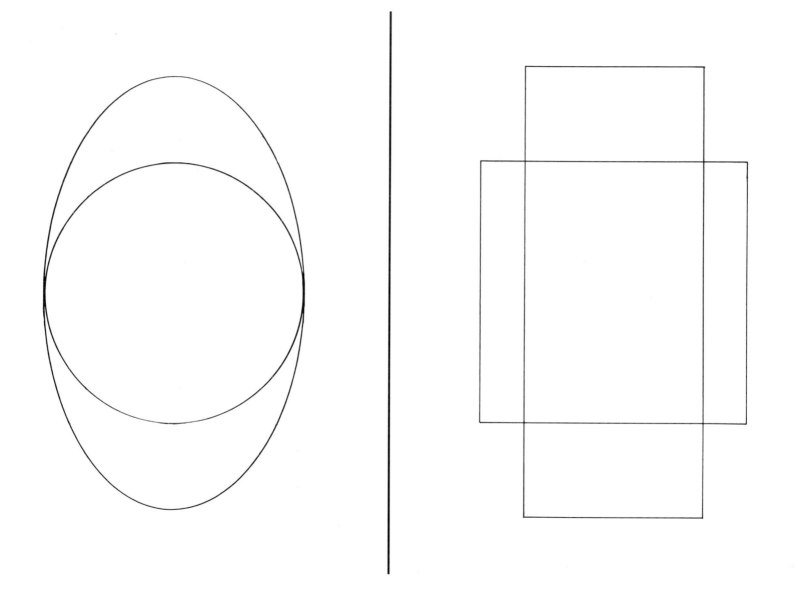

MENU

RECIPES

BUDGET

The End of Dinner
Jules Alexandre Grun (1868-1934)

Date of party

GUEST LIST

Replies

PLACEMENT

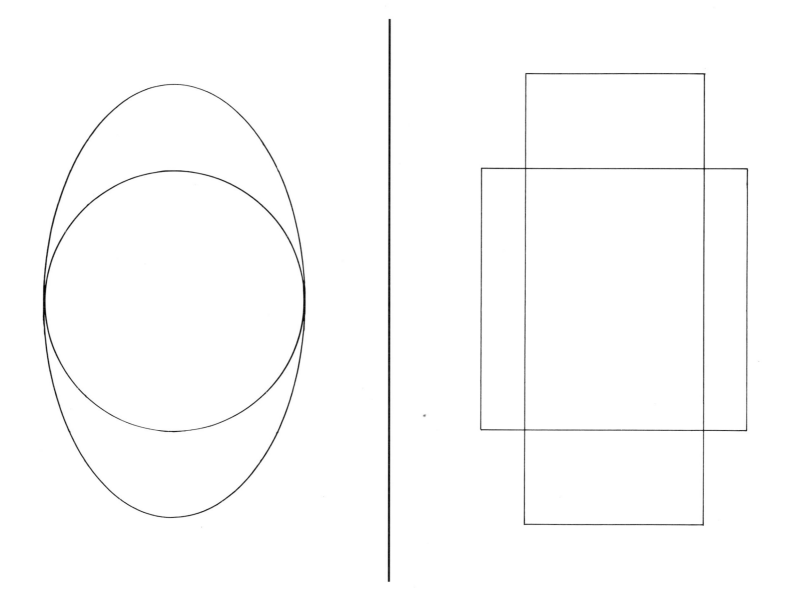

MENU

RECIPES

BUDGET

Still Life (detail)
Henri Roland de la Porte (1724-1793)

Date of party

GUEST LIST

Replies

PLACEMENT

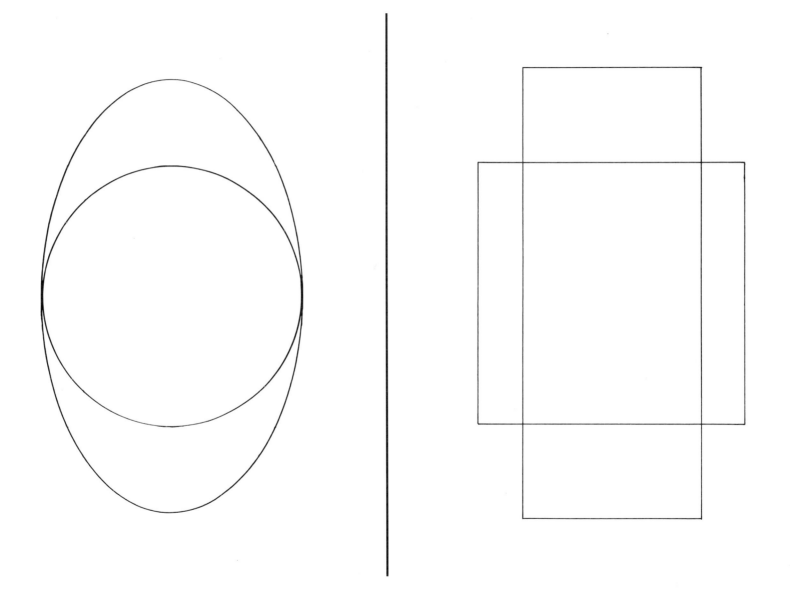

MENU

RECIPES

BUDGET

_____ | _____ | _____ | _____

_____ | _____ | _____ | _____

_____ | _____ | _____ | _____

_____ | _____ | _____ | _____

_____ | _____ | _____ | _____

_____ | _____ | _____ | _____

_____ | _____ | _____ | _____

_____ | _____ | _____ | _____

_____ | _____ | _____ | _____

_____ | _____ | _____ | _____

_____ | _____ | _____

Taking Tea
David Emil Joseph de Noter (b.1825)

_____ | _____ | _____

GUEST LIST

Date of party

Replies

_____

_____

_____

_____

_____

_____

_____

_____

_____

_____

_____

_____

_____

_____

PLACEMENT

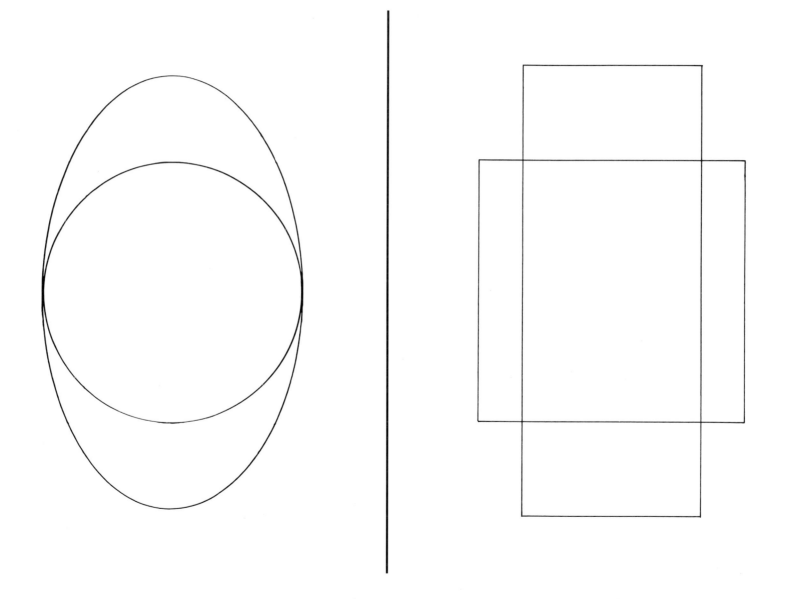

MENU

RECIPES

BUDGET

_____   _____   _____   _____

_____   _____   _____   _____

_____   _____   _____   _____

_____   _____   _____   _____

_____   _____   _____   _____

_____   _____   _____   _____

_____   _____   _____   _____

_____   _____   _____   _____

_____   _____   _____   _____

_____   _____   _____   _____

_____   _____   _____

Wrapped Oranges
William J McCloskey (1859-1941)
Acquisition in memory of Katrine Deak

_____   _____   _____

Name _____

Address _____

_____

Telephone _____

Name _____

Address _____

_____

Telephone _____

Name _____

Address _____

_____

Telephone _____

Name _____

Address _____

_____

Telephone _____

Name _____

Address _____

_____

Telephone _____

Name _____

Address _____

_____

Telephone _____

Name _____

Address _____

_____

Telephone _____

Name _____

Address _____

_____

Telephone _____

Name _____

Address _____

_____

Telephone _____

Name _____

Address _____

_____

Telephone _____

Name _____

Address _____

_____

Telephone _____

Name _____

Address _____

_____

Telephone _____

Name _____

Address _____

_____

Telephone _____

Name _____

Address _____

_____

Telephone _____

Name _____

Address _____

_____

Telephone _____

Name _____

Address _____

_____

Telephone _____

Name _____

Address _____

_____

Telephone _____

Name _____

Address _____

_____

Telephone _____

Name _____

Address _____

_____

Telephone _____

Name _____

Address _____

_____

Telephone _____

Name _____

Address _____

_____

Telephone _____

Name _____

Address _____

_____

Telephone _____

Name _____

Address _____

_____

Telephone _____

Name _____

Address _____

_____

Telephone _____

Name _____

Address _____

_____

Telephone _____

Name _____

Address _____

_____

Telephone _____

Name _____

Address _____

_____

Telephone _____

Name _____

Address _____

_____

Telephone _____

Name _____

Address _____

_____

Telephone _____

Name _____

Address _____

_____

Telephone _____

Name _____

Address _____

_____

Telephone _____

Name _____

Address _____

_____

Telephone _____

Name _____

Address _____

_____

Telephone _____

Name _____

Address _____

_____

Telephone _____

Name _____

Address _____

_____

Telephone _____

Name _____

Address _____

_____

Telephone _____

Name _____

Address _____

_____

Telephone _____

Name _____

Address _____

_____

Telephone _____

Name _____

Address _____

_____

Telephone _____

Name _____

Address _____

_____

Telephone _____

Name _____

Address _____

_____

Telephone _____

Name _____

Address _____

_____

Telephone _____

Name _____

Address _____

_____

Telephone _____

Name _____

Address _____

_____

Telephone _____

Name _____

Address _____

_____

Telephone _____

Name _____

Address _____

_____

Telephone _____

Name _____

Address _____

_____

Telephone _____

Name _____

Address _____

_____

Telephone _____

Name _____

Address _____

_____

Telephone _____

Name _____

Address _____

_____

Telephone _____

Name _____

Address _____

_____

Telephone _____

Name _____

Address _____

_____

Telephone _____

Name _____

Address _____

_____

Telephone _____

Name _____

Address _____

_____

Telephone _____

Name _____

Address _____

_____

Telephone _____

Name _____

Address _____

_____

Telephone _____

*The Publishers are very grateful to the following organisations,
individuals and institutions for their kind permission to reproduce their pictures:*
Amon Carter Museum, Musée des Beaux Arts de Lyon, Musée des Beaux Arts
Tourcoing, Bridgeman Art Library, Christies Colour Library, Gavin
Graham Gallery London, Harold Samuel Collection, Sir Alfred Munnings
Art Museum, Musées Nationaux France, National Gallery London, National
Gallery of Victoria, National Gallery of Art, Washington, Norton Simon Art
Foundation, Georges Pompidou Centre, Rafael Valls Gallery, Society for
Cultural Relations with the USSR.

Frontispiece:
A Maid in an Interior
David Emil Joseph de Noter (b.1825)

Cover:
Flowers and Fruit on a Table
Henri Fantin Latour (1836-1904)
Bequest of John T. Spaulding
Courtesy, Museum of Fine Arts, Boston

Published by Alan Hutchison Publishing Co
9 Pembridge Studios
27a Pembridge Villas
London W11 3EP

Worldwide distribution

Printed and bound in Hong Kong